M0001077728

OFFICIAL COCA-COLA Coca-Cola® **COLLECTORS SERIES**

Coca-Cola®
Collectible
Cars &
Trucks

THE OFFICIAL COCA-COLA COLLECTORS SERIES

Coca-Cola Collectible Bean Bags & Plush

Coca-Cola Collectible Cars & Trucks

Coca-Cola Collectible Polar Bears

Coca-Cola Collectible Santas

Coca-Cola®
Collectible
Cars &
Trucks

BECKETT PUBLICATIONS

Coca-Cola Collectible Cars and Trucks
Copyright ©2000 The Coca-Cola Company. All rights reserved.

All rights reserved under International and Pan-American Copyright Conventions. No part of this book shall be reproduced in any form or by any means, electronic or mechanical, including photocopying, recording, or by any information or retrieval system, without written permission from the copyright holder.

Published by:
Beckett Publications
15850 Dallas Parkway
Dallas, Texas 75248

ISBN: 1-887432-99-X
Beckett™ is a registered trademark of Beckett Publications

First Edition: September 2000
Beckett Corporate Sales and Information (972) 991-6657

The contributors to this publication have attempted to place current fair market value on each collectible. This book is to be used as a guide only. Prices in this guide reflect current retail rates determined just prior to printing. Prices are based on a grading system of 1–10 (with 10 being Mint and 1 being poor). As always, items are only worth what someone is willing to pay for them. Auction and dealer prices will vary based on condition, geographic location and demand. Neither the Authors nor the Publisher assumes responsibility for any losses that might be incurred through the sale or purchase of merchandise because of the information contained herein.

Many of the items listed in this book were never authorized by The Coca-Cola Company.

Printed in Canada

Contents

Introduction

By Kyle Foreman

" I'd like to buy the world a Coke"
— 1971 jingle

1940s — Los Angeles

I imagine most of us can remember back to our most cherished childhood gifts: a bicycle, "Rock'em Sock'em" Robots, a Barbie doll or a baseball mitt. The gift that I remember most is a beautiful shining Coca-Cola Ice Cream car that my parents gave me. That first gift was the beginning of what has become one of the most complete Coca-Cola cars and trucks collections in the country.

Coca-Cola has always been a love of mine from the start. Growing up in the Fifties, we would go to the filling station and put a nickel in the red Coke machine. I was always fascinated by the way the Coca-Cola script looked on the bottles. My friends and I would all look on the bottom of our bottles to check the city and state where it was bottled. The one with the bottle produced farthest away would win our game. There wasn't a prize for winning, but you would get the bragging rights.

When my Dad would send me to the station to fill up with gas, he would give me a dollar to fill up the five-gallon tank. I'd always put in ninety-five cents worth of gas, to leave me with a nickel for a bottle of Coke. One day my father said, "Son, you better tell the man at the gas station that he's off about a nickel on every five gallons." This was one of my first lessons in the world of high finance.

When I began collecting Coke vehicles, I collected trucks of all sizes. I especially liked the Smith-Miller, Buddy L and the miniature bottles and cases that came with the trucks. As I slowly added to my collection with different models, I decided to keep the vehicles in the original boxes which I later realized was a very good idea.

I have watched as the production of Coca-Cola toy cars and trucks has grown overseas each year. These vehicles are now made in

1968 — Belgium

Germany, England, Italy, France, Japan and Hong Kong to name a few. These foreign-made toys are often scarce in the United States, making them more valuable. But these imports have added to the toys collectors can choose from.

With this explosion in the industry, more new Coke toys are on the market, making these affordable to younger collectors. But even with the newest Coca-Cola car or truck, it's worth buying today because it will become tomorrow's collectible.

Every item in this book has been given two prices: 8 (near Mint) condition and not in the original packaging; and 10 (Mint) condition with its original packaging. This will hopefully give a realistic market range for secondary value of these Coke collectibles.

It is a pleasure for me to share with you my joy for Coca-Cola cars and trucks, and I hope that you will find the treasure that you are looking for. And, remember, for these collectibles, the excitement is in the hunt.

1945 – California

CHAPTER 1

Coca-Cola Trucks

1969–1970 — Louisiana

The Standardization Committee of Bottlers of Coca-Cola, originally organized in 1924, is charged with setting uniform standards for equipment and to provide standard colors, insignia, etc., for the bottlers of Coca-Cola. The Standardization Committee's decisions regarding truck fleet insignia design and lettering set Coca-Cola apart from other soda products and stoked my collecting interest as a small boy in the 1950s.

More so, the now-famous colors "red-DW 618," "white-B 713," and "yellow-DW 583" adopted by the Committee and adorned on every form of Coca-Cola product, equipment and advertisement, have become the same colors to which many Americans identify their fondest childhood memories.

The Coca-Cola Company knew that whether Coke was advertised on the side of a local bottler's truck fleet or on the side of a Smith-Miller truck, Coke was being promoted to the masses. As a boy my prized possession was my Smith-Miller bottle truck, which prompted "Drink Ice Cold Coca-Cola" on its side and on every bottle crate. It never really occurred to me that I was helping to promote Coca-Cola when my friends and I played with my truck.

Somehow the unique design and color of my truck (which closely matched the delivery trucks of the day) stuck with me through the years and most probably enhanced my Coca-Cola collecting interest. Today, other collectors share similar childhood stories with me. I often wonder if the 1924 Standardization Committee of Bottlers of Coca-Cola knew just what they were creating when they began setting the Coca-Cola standards that have become a very important part of our culture.

The interest in collecting Coca-Cola vehicles began in earnest in the 1930s when The Metalcraft Corporation of St. Louis, Missouri, began making eleven-inch-long "Bottling Trucks" patterned after the Coca-Cola delivery trucks of the day. These trucks, which advertised "Coca-Cola—Every Bottle Sterilized," were well made, usually employing heavy steel construction, rubber tires, and a baked enamel finish.

What makes these trucks rare today is their cargo, ten miniature glass Coca-Cola bottles filled with Coke and topped with a mini bottle cap! These trucks are considered the Holy Grail of Coca-Cola vehicle collecting, especially when found with their boxes in Mint condition. Collectors are so enthusiastic about these trucks that prices range well over $1,500 for near Mint examples. Today's advanced collector looks for the several different variations that were produced during this period, such as metal wheels, working headlights, and the "long front" truck design.

In the late 1940s and into the 1950s, Smith-Miller (then Marx), Buddy L and several other toy manufacturers were granted licenses to produce toy vehicles. These well-made trucks and cars, all with the identifying colors and logos, helped the next generation of kids to associate their fondest childhood memories with Coke.

In the 1940s, Smith-Miller produced a delivery truck with a metal body and a wooden bed. By the 1950s, all-metal trucks were the norm. Many trucks came with a cargo of Coca-Cola in crates, some even came with small metal handcarts making these vehicles prized possessions for collectors today. Because of the variety and quality of vehicles produced at this time, this era is considered the heyday of Coke vehicles and examples from this period often take prominent positions in collections today.

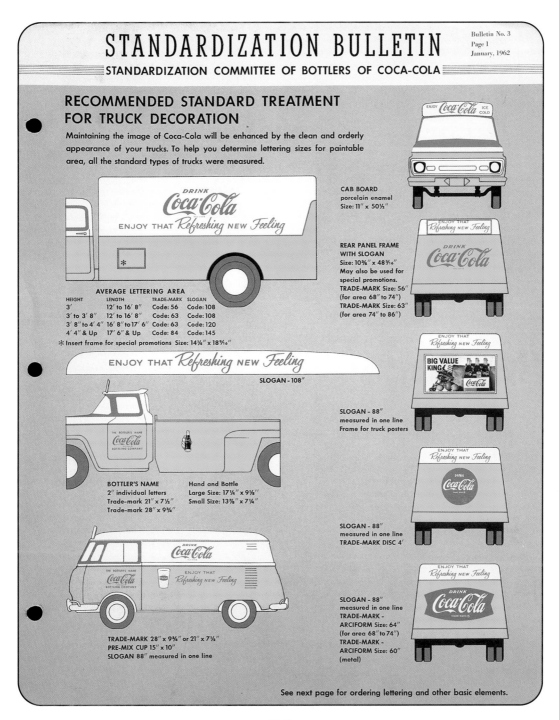

STANDARDIZATION BULLETIN

STANDARDIZATION COMMITTEE OF BOTTLERS OF COCA-COLA

RECOMMENDED STANDARD TREATMENT FOR TRUCK DECORATION

Maintaining the image of Coca-Cola will be enhanced by the clean and orderly appearance of your trucks. To help you determine lettering sizes for paintable area, all the standard types of trucks were measured.

DRINK **Coca-Cola**
ENJOY THAT *Refreshing* NEW *Feeling*

CAB BOARD
porcelain enamel
Size: 11" x 50½"

REAR PANEL FRAME WITH SLOGAN
Size: 10⅜" x 48⁹⁄₁₆"
May also be used for special promotions.
TRADE-MARK Size: 56"
(for area 68" to 74")
TRADE-MARK Size: 63"
(for area 74" to 86")

AVERAGE LETTERING AREA

HEIGHT	LENGTH	TRADE-MARK	SLOGAN
3'	12' to 16' 8"	Code: 56	Code: 108
3' to 3' 8"	12' to 16' 8"	Code: 63	Code: 108
3' 8" to 4' 4"	16' 8" to 17' 6"	Code: 63	Code: 120
4' 4" & Up	17' 6" & Up	Code: 84	Code: 145

✳ Insert frame for special promotions Size: 14¼" x 18⁹⁄₁₆"

ENJOY THAT *Refreshing* NEW *Feeling*
SLOGAN - 108"

THE BOTTLER'S NAME **Coca-Cola** BOTTLING COMPANY

BOTTLER'S NAME
2" individual letters
Trade-mark 21" x 7½"
Trade-mark 28" x 9¾"

Hand and Bottle
Large Size: 17¼" x 9⅛"
Small Size: 13⅞" x 7¼"

SLOGAN - 88"
measured in one line
Frame for truck posters

BIG VALUE KING

SLOGAN - 88"
measured in one line
TRADE-MARK DISC 4'

DRINK **Coca-Cola**

SLOGAN - 88"
measured in one line
TRADE-MARK - ARCIFORM Size: 64"
(for area 68" to 74")
TRADE-MARK - ARCIFORM Size: 60"
(metal)

DRINK **Coca-Cola**
ENJOY THAT *Refreshing* NEW *Feeling*
THE BOTTLER'S NAME **Coca-Cola** BOTTLING COMPANY

TRADE-MARK 28" x 9¾" or 21" x 7½"
PRE-MIX CUP 15" x 10"
SLOGAN 88" measured in one line

ENJOY **Coca-Cola** ICE COLD

See next page for ordering lettering and other basic elements.

1962

In the late 1950s and into the 1960s, an even greater variety of Coca-Cola vehicles began to appear, often made of tin or plastic. While these cars and trucks were generally cheaper than previous issues, they still had that identifying color scheme and logo that endeared them to

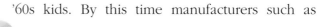

'60s kids. By this time manufacturers such as Nylint, Marx, Buddy L and an ever-increasing number of foreign companies (especially Japanese) began to produce vehicles all with the Coca-Cola trademark. Further, other Coke products such as Sprite and Tab began to appear with regularity on the sides of toy vehicles. Because of the generally lower quality of production material used for these vehicles, collectors from this era have a harder time finding Mint examples of 1960s Coca-Cola vehicles.

The youngest collectors, those who grew up in the 1970s and 1980s, can easily associate their childhood memories with the unique vehicles of this time. Those have included semi-tractor trailers and Volkswagens along with Coke can-shaped racers and even a race-car pillow! Now NASCAR and Coca-Cola have teamed up with several stock car offerings. While these vehicles do not command the prices of previous Coca-Cola collectibles, they are still interesting and will, one day, take their place as valued and appreciated collectibles.

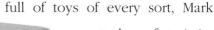

But the question remains, why do people collect Coca-Cola vehicles? Earlier this year I was attending a toy show in Chicago with my good friend Mark Leinberger. As we walked along the rows of tables full of toys of every sort, Mark spotted a futuristic-looking "Big Wheel" Coca-Cola truck from 1973 and reminisced that he played for hours at a time with an

identical one as a child. I guess that's when it dawned on me why people collect Coca-Cola.

For the past one hundred years each generation has had its own childhood memories of different Coca-Cola advertisements, collectibles and especially toys. Whether your generation played with a red and yellow Metalcraft Bottling Truck with glass bottles from the 1930s or a yellow Smith-Miller truck with plastic cases from the 1950s as I did, the one underlying feature common to all was Coca-Cola, that great American soft drink and icon of generations. Yes, maybe the Standardization Committee of Bottlers of Coca-Cola knew just what they were doing in 1924, when they along with selling soda started selling memories.

Coca-Cola Trucks

● **1932 METALCRAFT DELIVERY TRUCK #171**

Made in USA
Material: Pressed Steel
Length: 11 inches
Notes: The Metalcraft
Company began
making toys in the late
1920s and continued
until 1935. The
Metalcraft Coke trucks
were made from 1931 to 1935

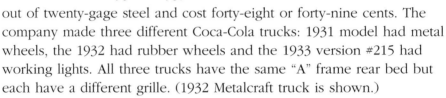

out of twenty-gage steel and cost forty-eight or forty-nine cents. The
company made three different Coca-Cola trucks: 1931 model had metal
wheels, the 1932 had rubber wheels and the 1933 version #215 had
working lights. All three trucks have the same "A" frame rear bed but
each have a different grille. (1932 Metalcraft truck is shown.)

Value (8 condition): $1,000
Mint condition: $1,600
Mint condition in box: $2,800

● **1931 METALCRAFT DELIVERY TRUCK WITH METAL WHEELS**

(Not shown)
Value: 8 condition: $600
Mint condition: $900
Mint condition in box: $1,500

● **1933 METALCRAFT DELIVERY TRUCK WITH WORKING LIGHTS**

(Not shown)
Value: 8 condition: $1,400
Mint condition: $2,500
Mint condition in box: $3,100

● **1934 METALCRAFT DELIVERY TRUCK**

(Not shown)
Value: 8 condition: $1,400
Mint condition: $2,500
Mint condition in box: $3,700

● 1950s AM-BO ON-POWER DELIVERY TRUCK

Made in Italy
Material: Tin
Length: 4 inches
Notes: This is a very rare
truck and is almost never
in Mint condition.

Value: Out of box (8 condition): $800
Mint condition in box: $950

● 1950s ASC FRICTION POWER COCA-COLA TRANSPORT
TRAILER

Made in Japan
Material: Tin
Length: 8³⁄₄ inches
Notes: This truck was available in a boxed set of
six vehicles including
a fire truck, school
bus, Greyhound bus,
pie truck and Coca-
Cola truck. The value
for the set is $1,800 MIB.

Value: Out of box (8 condition): $800
Mint condition in box: $1,000

● 1950s CRAGSTAN FRICTION POWER DELIVERY
TRUCK

Made in Japan
Material: Tin and Plastic
Length: 4 inches
Notes: These came in the Tiny Giant
Friction Power boxed set of twelve
assorted toy vehicles, including Jeeps,
racecars and fire trucks.

Value: Out of box (8 condition): $150
Mint condition in box: $175

● 1950s HAJI FRICTION POWER DELIVERY TRUCK

Made in Japan
Material: Tin
Length: 4½ inches
Notes: This truck is hard to find but usually is in good condition.

Value: Out of box (8 condition): $600
Mint condition in box: $900

● 1950s LESNEY/MATCHBOX DELIVERY TRUCK #37

Material: Die Cast
Length: 2¼ inches
Notes: This 1950s truck had gray wheels and an uneven load, and cost forty-nine cents.

Value: Out of box (8 condition): $140
Mint condition in box: $185

● 1950–1960 LESNEY DELIVERY TRUCKS

Made in England
Material: Die Cast
Length: 2½ inches
Notes: When this truck came out it was very collectible, which is why you can often still find it in its original box. The trucks with the gray wheels are more valuable than the trucks with black

wheels. Truck #37-A has an uneven load and its the most valuable variation.

Value: Out of box (8 condition): $45
Mint condition in box: $150

● 1950s LINEMAR FRICTION POWER DELIVERY TRUCK

Made in Japan
Material: Tin
Length: 5 inches

Value: Out of box (8 condition): $450
Mint condition in box: $600

● 1950s LINEMAR SQUASH CAB FRICTION POWER TRUCK

Material: Tin
Length: 3 inches
Notes: The set of twelve Squash Cab Friction trucks in the box is valued at $850.

Value: Out of box (8 condition): $175
Mint condition in box: $250

● 1950s LOUIS MARX CO. SPRITE BOY DELIVERY TRUCK

Made in USA

Material: Pressed Steel

Length: 20¼ inches

Notes: This yellow stake truck featuring the Sprite Boy has no rear decal. The first Coke truck produced by Louis Marx was the Sprite Boy stake truck model #991, introduced in the late 1940s.

Value: Out of box (8 condition): $350
Mint condition in box: $700

● 1950s LOUIS MARX CO. DELIVERY TRUCK

Made in USA

Material: Pressed Steel

Length: 20¼ inches

Value: Out of box (8 condition): $500
Mint condition in box: $900

● 1950s MARX DELIVERY TRUCK BOX

Made in USA

Size: 18 inches by 6 inches by 8½ inches

Value: $400

● 1950s PYRO PLASTIC CORP. DELIVERY TRUCK

Made in USA
Material: Plastic
Length: 5½ inches
Notes: Originally cost 29 cents and came with either smooth or knobby wheels. This very collectible piece is difficult to find without chips, cracks and breaks in the plastic.

Value: Out of box (8 condition): $90
Mint condition in box: $200

● 1950s ROSKO FRICTION POWER DELIVERY TRUCK

Made in Japan
Material: Tin
Length: 8 inches
Notes: This truck was also available as a Canada Dry delivery vehicle. It's value is half that of the Coca-Cola version.

Value: Out of box (8 condition): $700
Mint condition in box: $850

1950s SCHILDKROT PULL TOY DELIVERY TRUCK

Made in Germany
Material: Plastic
Length: 15 inches
Notes: There were three variations of this truck, which were made for the Holland toy market. This truck came with eight plastic cases.

Value: Out of box (8 condition): $375
Mint condition in box: $650

1950s TT FRICTION POWER DELIVERY TRUCK

Made in Japan
Material: Tin
Length: 4 inches
Notes: This Coca-Cola van bread truck came in a box of twelve assorted trucks. The value of all twelve trucks Mint in box is $650.

Value: Out of box (8 condition): $125
Mint condition in box: $200

● 1950 CRAGSTAN TOYS TINY GIANT DELIVERY TRUCK

Made in Japan
Material: Tin and Plastic
Length: 4 inches

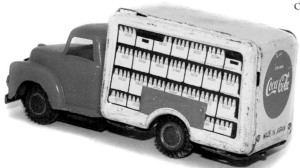

Notes: This friction power truck came in two variations: a red plastic cab and a yellow tin cab. Both variations have the same value.

Value: Out of box (8 condition): $100 Mint condition in box: $175

● 1950, 1952 GOSO WIND-UP DELIVERY TRUCK

Made in Germany
Material: Tin
Size: 8¼ inches
Notes: This truck came with eight metal cases and also could come with black trim. The 1949 model said, "Made in US Zone Germany" in small print on the side. The model with black trim has headlights on top of the finders. The model with red trim has headlights below the fenders.

*Value: Out of box (8 condition): $1,800
Mint condition in box: $2,500*

● 1950–1954 LOUIS MARX CO. SNUB NOSE DELIVERY TRUCK

Made in USA
Material: Plastic
Length: 11 inches
Notes: The Snub Nose
Coca-Cola truck by Marx
is one of the most diffi-
cult Coke vehicles to
find. Many of the earlier
plastic trucks are easily broken or cracked. It came with six plastic
cases and a hand truck. The side door of this truck opens and closes.

Value: Out of box
(8 condition): $500
Mint condition in
box: $750

● 1955 WIKING COCA-COLA DELIVERY TRUCK

Material: Plastic
Length: 3½ inches
Notes: These trucks came in
two color variations.

Value: Out of box (8
condition): $125
Mint condition in
box: $175

● 1954, 1956 LOUIS MARX CO. DELIVERY TRUCK #21

Made in USA
Material: Tin
Length: 12½ inches
Notes: This truck came with six yellow plastic cases with green bottles. There were three variations of this truck: with cases and bottles; with cases, bottles and a hand truck; with cases, bottles, a hand truck and horns on the top of the truck cab.

*Value: Out of box
(8 condition): $350
Mint condition in box:
$600*

● 1956–1957 LOUIS MARX CO. DELIVERY TRUCK #1089

Made in USA
Material: Pressed Steel
Length: 17½ inches
Notes: One of the large Marx trucks, for this model Louis Marx used the same #22 cab but with a different trailer.

Value: Out of box (8 condition): $550
Mint condition in box: $950

● 1956–1957 LOUIS MARX CO. DELIVERY TRUCK #1090

Made in USA
Material: Tin
Length: 17½ inches
Notes: This No. 22 Marx Delivery Truck came with fifteen to twenty-four yellow cases with green bottles and a red or yellow hand truck, depending on year. Most

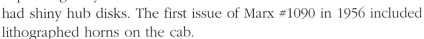

had shiny hub disks. The first issue of Marx #1090 in 1956 included lithographed horns on the cab.

Value: Out of box (8 condition): $800
Mint condition in box: $1,200

● 1956–57 LOUIS MARX CO. DELIVERY TRUCK

Made in USA
Material: Tin
Length: 17½ inches

Value: Out of box (8 condition): $600
Mint condition in box: $1,000

● 1956–1966 TCO (TIPP & CO.) VW FRICTION POWER DELIVERY TRUCK

Made in Germany
Material: Tin
Length: 9 inches
Notes: This export version came in both English and German versions and had five cases with removable red and clear bottles. Some variations came with a driver, wind-up billboard and wind-up power.

Value: Out of box (8 condition): $650
Mint condition in box: $800

● 1960s AM-BO DELIVERY TRUCKS

Made in Italy
Material: Tin
Length: 4 inches
Notes: These trucks were available in boxes and blister packs. There were three variations of these trucks: tin wheels (value: $650–800), smooth wheels (value: $450–550) and knobby wheels.

Value: Out of box (8 condition): $400 (knobby wheels)
Mint condition in box: $500 (knobby wheels)

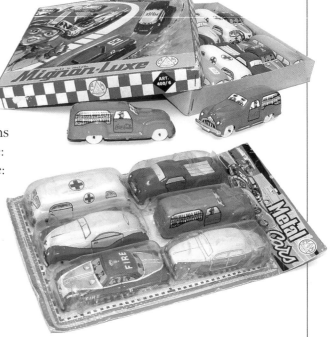

● 1960s BUDDY L DELIVERY TRUCK

Made in USA
Material: Pressed Steel
Length: 15 inches
Notes: This truck came with wrap-around bumpers, two metal hand trucks and eight green and red cases with green bottles. This was the first version of the new Ford style and is the hardest to find.

Value: Out of box (8 condition): $250
Mint condition in box: $550

● 1960 BUDDY L DELIVERY TRUCK

Made in USA
Material: Pressed Steel
Length: 15 inches
Notes: This truck came with a chrome grille, two metal hand trucks and eight red cases with green bottles.

Value: Out of box (8 condition): $150
Mint condition in box: $400

● 1960s JOUETS/CAMION BRASSEUR REMOTE CONTROL DELIVERY TRUCK

Made in France
Material: Plastic
Length: 10½ inches
Notes: This truck was made in France and is very difficult to find, especially with all of its parts. The truck is also very fragile, so it is nearly impossible to find it in a 10 condition. It came with ten yellow and red cases and a hand truck.

Value: Out of box (8 condition): $1,000
Mint condition in box: $1,800

● 1960s MOLTO DELIVERY TRUCK

Made in Spain
Material: Plastic
Length: 7⅓ inches
Notes: This pull toy truck was made for the beach or sandbox. It came with eight green cases with red and clear bottles.

Value: Out of box (8 condition): $75
Mint condition in box: $150

● 1960s SANYO BATTERY OPERATED DELIVERY TRUCK

Made in Japan
Material: Tin
Length: 12½ inches
Notes: This yellow version of the Coca-Cola battery operated route truck came in two different box variations. One variation had block letters on the packaging; the other used the standard Coca-Cola script. This truck also came in a very difficult to find red and white variation.

Value: Out of box (8 condition): $350
Mint condition in box: $450

● 1960s SANYO BATTERY OPERATED ROUTE TRUCK – RED AND WHITE

Made in Japan
Material: Tin
Length: 12½ inches
Notes: The red version of this truck is difficult to find.

Value: Out of box (8 condition): $475
Mint condition in box: $650

● 1960s SESAME DELIVERY VEHICLES

Made in Spain
Material: Tin and Plastic
Length: 3¼ inches
Notes: Came in three variations of Coca-Cola trucks. Also came in Friction Power, a box of six different cars and trucks valued at $700.

Value: Out of box (8 condition): $175
Mint condition in box: $275

● 1960s SESAME DELIVERY VAN

Made in France
Material: Tin and Plastic
Size: 5 inches
Notes: Came in a box of six vehicles. The larger scale is very rare.

Value: Out of box (8 condition): $450
Mint condition in box: $650

● 1960s TAIYO VOLKSWAGEN FRICTION POWER VEHICLE

Made in Japan
Material: Tin
Length: 8½ inches
Notes: Two variations of this vehicle were made—one has a blue windshield.
Value: Out of box (8 condition): $350
Mint condition in box: $475

● 1960 N WIND-UP ICE CREAM SODA TRUCK SODA CAR

Made in Japan
Material: Tin
Length: 4¼ inches
Notes: This is one of the nicest Coke toy vehicles around. Most of these were sold in France.

Value: Out of box (8 condition): $450
Mint condition in box: $750

● 1970s BUDDY L DELIVERY TRUCK

Made in USA
Material: Steel
Length: 9⅛ inches

Notes: There were two variations of this truck: with chrome hubcaps and white hubcaps. The truck with chrome hubs came with a metal hand truck and ten red mini cases with green bottles. The truck with white hubs came with a metal hand truck and only five cases. In 1970, The Coca-Cola Company introduced the new dynamic contour logo. The Buddy L was the first Coca-Cola truck to display the new logo.

Value: Out of box (8 condition): $75
Mint condition in box: $125

● 1970s CORGI DELIVERY TRUCKS

Made in Great Britain
Material: Die Cast
Length: 2½ inches to 3 inches

Value: Out of box (8 condition): $10
Mint condition in box: $20

● 1970s CORGI JUNIORS CHEVY DELIVERY VAN

Made in England
Material: Die Cast
Length: 2½ to 3 inches
Notes: This also came in a double-decker bus.

Value: Out of box (8 condition): $10
Mint condition in box: $20

1970s DURHAM INDUSTRIES ZIP ALONG/ROLL ALONG COKE TRUCK

Made in Hong Kong
Material: Plastic
Length: 4½ inches
Scale: 1/55

Notes: This truck also came in yellow and white Zip-Along/Roll Along trucks.

Value: Out of box (8 condition): $20
Mint condition in box: $45

1970s FRICTION POWER MOVING VAN

Made in Hong Kong
Material: Plastic
Length: 5½ inches
Notes: This came in three different colors and with three different labels. The set of three is valued at $250–350.

Value: Out of box (8 condition): $175
Mint condition in box: $200

1970s IMPALA LARGE DELIVERY TRUCK

Made in Mexico
Material: Plastic and Metal
Length: 14 inches
Notes: This truck had numerous multi-colored Coke cases and "Fiesta" written on the back and "Tome Coca-Cola Bien Fria" on the side.

Value: Out of box (8 condition): $100
Mint condition in box: $200

● 1970s MAXWELL DELIVERY TRUCK

Made in India
Material: Die Cast
Length: 3¾ inches

*Value: Out of box
(8 condition): $35
Mint condition in box: $50*

● 1970s MAXWELL CO. ON-POWER DELIVERY VAN

Made in India
Material: Die Cast
Length: 3¾ inches
Notes: This vehicle came with two different logos. One has the dynamic ribbon logo; the other does not.

*Value: Out of box
(8 condition): $40
Mint condition in box: $65*

● 1970s RICO DELIVERY TRUCK

Made in Spain
Material: Steel and Plastic
Length: 5¾ inches

*Value: Out of box (8 condition): $165
Mint condition in box: $250*

● 1970s TAIYO BIG WHEEL DELIVERY TRUCK

Made in Japan
Material: Plastic and Tin
Length: 10¼ inches
Notes: This battery-operated Bump 'N Go Action truck came in three variations. The difference in the three is the text on the sides of the vehicles between the wheels. One has "Coca-Cola Bottling Co." the second has "New York Bottling Co." and the third has "Atlanta Bottling Co." There is no difference in the value of these three.

Value: Out of box (8 condition): $90
Mint condition in box: $135

● 1970s TT FRICTION POWER DELIVERY TRUCK

Material: Tin and Plastic

Length: 3¾ inches

Notes: This Coca-Cola friction power truck has a variation with "refreshing" misspelled. There is also a variation with an unusual red cab.

Value: Out of box (8 condition): $30

Mint condition in box: $45

● 1970s UNI-PLAST GMC DELIVERY TRUCK

Made in Mexico

Material: Plastic

Length: 7½ inches

Notes: This truck came with eight yellow, red or white cases with brown bottles. The detail is very good on this GMC truck.

Value: Out of box (8 condition): $300

Mint condition in box: $450

● 1970s VAN GOODIES FORD DENIMACHINE VAN

Made in Canada
Material: Plastic and wood mix/faux wood
Length: 12 inches

Value: Out of box
(8 condition): $200
Mint condition in box: $300

● DENIMACHINE VAN POSTER

Notes: The Denimachine
Ford van was custom
designed by Hot Rod
magazine. Ten of these
vans were built and given
away as a promotion in
the 1970s.

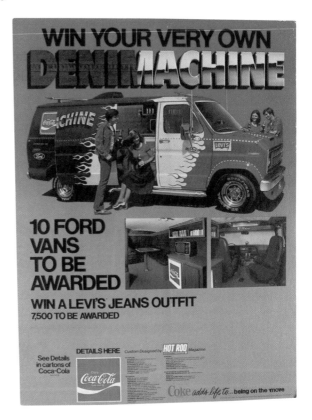

● 1970s WINROSS TRACTOR TRAILER

Made in USA
Material: Die Cast
Length: 9⅜ inches
Notes: This white trac-
tor-trailer came in three
rear door color varia-
tions: red, silver and
white.

Value: Out of box (8 condition): $150
Mint condition in box: $200

● 1970s YAXON TRACTOR TRAILER

Made in Italy
Material: Die Cast
and Plastic
Length: 13 inches
Scale: ⅟₄₃
Notes: Paper
decals are on
the trailer.

Value: Out of box (8 condition): $200
Mint condition in box: $325

● 1970 CORGI CHEVY DELIVERY VAN

Made in England
Material: Die Cast
Length: 2½ inches

*Value: Out of box
(8 condition): $10
Mint condition in box:
$20*

● 1970 CORGI TURBO RACING TEAM TRUCK, TRAILER AND CAR

Made in Great Britain
Material: Die Cast
Length: 10½ inches

Value: Out of box (8 condition): $30
Mint condition in box: $65

● 1970 EUROPA/LUCKY BATTERY OPERATED VW WAGON

Made in Hong Kong
  Material: Plastic
  Length: 4½ inches
  Notes: This vehicle was made
  for the German market.

*Value: Out of box
(8 condition): $100*
Mint condition in box: $175

● 1978 CORGI CHEVY VAN

Made in England
Material: Die Cast
Length: 4¾ inches
Notes: This is a fairly common Coke vehicle that can still be found at yard sales and collectible stores. This van has a rear door that opens and reveals what looks like cases of Coca-Cola.

Value: Out of box (8 condition): $35
Mint condition in box: $65

● 1978 NOSTALGIC MINIATURE DELIVERY TRUCK

Made in USA
Material: Die Cast
Length: 5¼ inches

*Value: Out of box
(8 condition): $100
Mint condition in box:
$125*

● 1978–79 UNI-PLAST DELIVERY TRUCK #302

Made in Mexico
Material: Plastic
Length: 9½ inches

*Value: Out of box (8 condition):
$85
Mint condition in box: $150*

● 1979 CORGI DELIVERY TEAM SET

Made in Great Britain
Material: Die Cast
Length: 3 inches

*Value: Out of box
(8 condition): $15 (set)
Mint condition in box: $35 (set)*

● 1979 CORGI SUPER HAULER TRACTOR TRAILER

Made in Great Britain
Material: Die Cast
Length: 9½ inches

Notes: This truck was built by Corgi Toys Ltd., but was distributed by Hartoy Inc.

Value: Out of box (8 condition): $35
Mint condition in box: $50

● 1979 LESNEY MATCHBOX K–31 SUPER KINGS PETERBUILT TRUCK

Made in England
Material: Die Cast
Length: 12¼ inches

Notes: There are three variations of this truck: an all-white top on the cab, a chrome AC top on the cab and a white AC top on the cab. This truck can still be found at collectible shows.

Value: Out of box (8 condition): $20
Mint condition in box: $35

1979 LESNEY MODELS OF YESTERYEAR (#Y12 NEW YORK 75TH)

Made in England
Material: Die Cast
Length: 3½ inches
Notes: This truck was made with three variations.

The first is the #Y12 New York 75th Anniversary model, the most valuable of the variations. The second variation has the same color wheels as the 75th Anniversary model, and the third variation has darker colored wheels.

Value: Out of box (8 condition): $80
Mint condition in box: $150

1979 SMITH-MILLER YELLOW GMC DELIVERY TRUCK

Made in USA
Material: Cast Metal
Length: 14 inches
Notes: The parts for this truck were made in 1953 and 1954 but the truck wasn't assembled until 1979. Fred Thompson discovered 150 yellow GMC Coca-Cola trucks that had been painted and decaled in 1953 and were ready to be assembled. The Smith-Miller truck came with six cases of twenty-four bottles each.

Value: Out of box (8 condition): $750
Mint condition in box: $1,000

● 1979 SMITH-MILLER RED GMC DELIVERY TRUCK

Made in USA

Material: Cast Metal

Length: 14 inches

Notes: The brightly polished aluminum rear plate and billboard plate were the only parts manufactured for this truck in 1979. The rest of the truck was built from new-old stock. Fifty of these trucks were put together in 1979, each was numbered 1–50 on its frame. The Smith-Miller truck came with six cases of twenty-four bottles each.

Value: Out of box (8 condition): $1,400
Mint condition in box: $1,850

● 1970–1980 DURHAM INDUSTRIES ZIP ALONG/ROLL ALONG TRUCKS

Made in Hong Kong

Material: Plastic

Length: 4½ inches each

Notes: These trucks came with different body and wheel colors as well as different logos.

Value: Out of box (8 condition): $30
Mint condition in box: $45

● 1980s BRUMM-GLAMOUR COCA-COLA FIAT TRUCK

Made in Italy
Material: Die Cast
Scale: 1/43

Value: Out of box (8 condition): $30
Mint condition in box: $75

● 1980s BRUMM-GLAMOUR DELIVERY TRUCK

Made in Italy
Material: Die Cast
Scale: 1/43
Notes: This truck is still fairly easy to find.

Value: Out of box (8 condition): $40
Mint condition in box: $85

● 1980s BUDDY L COCA-COLA TRUCK AND TRAILER

Material: Steel and Plastic
Length: 14 inches
Notes: This truck came with eight red cases, green bottles and a Coca-Cola machine. There are variations of the truck with or without the sunroof and with two different slogans on the side, "Coke Is It," and "Have A Coke And A Smile."

Value: Out of box (8 condition): $20

● 1980s BUDDY L DELIVERY TRUCK

Made in USA
Material: Steel
Length 4¾ inches
Notes: This truck came with two plastic cases. There were three variations of this Buddy L truck.

Value: Out of box (8 condition): $10
Mint condition in box: $20

● 1980s BUDDY L DELIVERY TRUCK SET #666H

Made in USA
Material: Steel
Notes: This is a fifteen-piece set that included ten red cases with green bottles, two hand trucks, a figure and two vehicles.

Value: Out of box (8 condition): $30
Mint condition in box: $45

● 1980s BUDDY L DELIVERY TRUCK SET

Made in USA
Material: Steel
Notes: This is a seven-piece set that included a 4¾ inch long truck with two cases, a 10½ inch truck with five cases and a hand truck, a forklift, three red cases with green bottles and a steel loading ramp.

Value: Out of box (8 condition): $75

● 1980s BUDDY L TRACTOR TRAILER

Made in USA
Material: Steel
Length: 14 inches
Notes: This truck
came with eight
red cases holding
green bottles and
one Coca-Cola
machine. The
trailer had several

different slogan variations: "It's the Real Thing" and "Coke is it!" It
also came with or without the sunroof.

Value: Out of box (8 condition): $35
Mint condition in box: $50

● 1980s BUDGIE VW COCA-COLA PICKUP

Made in UK
Material: Die Cast
Scale: 1/43

Value: Out of box (8 condition): $35
Mint condition in box: $45

● 1980s COCA-COLA TRUCK AND TRAILER

Made in Spain
Material: Plastic
Length: 8 inches

Value: Out of box (8 condition): $30
Mint condition in box: $55

● 1980s COKE 1930s–1940s DELIVERY VAN

Material: Cast Iron
Length: 3¾ inches
Notes: This truck is still fairly easy to find.

Value: Out of box (8 condition): $3

Mint condition in box: $8

● 1980s DAIYA ISUZU TRUCK

Made in Japan
Material: Plastic
Length: 12 inches
Notes: This truck came with nine yellow plastic cases with green bottles and a hand truck. The bed of the truck has clock-work cargo doors with friction power.

Value: Out of box (8 condition): $200

Mint condition in box: $350

● 1980s DELHAR DISTRIBUTORS SUPER WHEELS SET

Material: Die Cast
Length: 2¾ inches

Value: Out of box (8 condition): $25
Mint condition in box: $45

● 1980s DGM MORRIS TRUCK

Made in England
Material: Die Cast
Length: 3¾ inches
Scale: 1/43

Notes: There are eight variations of this truck with different body styles, colors and wheels.

Value: Out of box (8 condition): $55
Mint condition in box: $80

● 1980s KINGSTAR FORD ECONOLINE E–150 VAN

Made in Korea
Material: Die Cast
Scale: 1/60
Notes: Also was available in yellow, silver and red.

Value: Out of box (8 condition): $35
Mint condition in box: $50

● 1980s K-LINE COCA-COLA TRACTOR TRAILER

Material: Die Cast
Scale: 1/49

Value: Out of box (8 condition): $40
Mint condition in box: $75

● 1980s LARAMI KING OF THE ROAD TRUCK

Material: Plastic and Die Cast

Length: 2¾ inches

Notes: The King of the Road trucks were available in different colors including: green, blue, brown, white, and yellow.

Value: Out of box (8 condition): $10
Mint condition in box: $25

● 1980s LIEDO DAYS GONE BY VEHICLE COLLECTION

Made in England

Material: Die Cast

Length: 2½ to 4½ inches

Value: Out of box (8 condition): $15
Mint condition in box: $20

● 1980s LIEDO DELIVERY TRUCKS

Made in Great Britain

Material: Die Cast

Length: 4½ inches

Notes: There were more than sixteen body styles and color variations of these trucks.

Value: Out of box (8 condition): $10

Mint condition in box: $20

● 1980s MAXITOYS OLD-TIMER MODEL FORD TRUCK

Made in Holland

Material: Metal

Length: 11 inches

Notes: Only about five hundred of these were made.

Value: Out of box (8 condition): $450

Mint condition in box: $550

● 1980s MINIBRINDES MINI MACK

Made in Brazil

Material: Metal

Length: 7 inches

Value: Out of box (8 condition): $80

Mint condition in box: $150

● 1980s NOSTALGIC MINIATURE BOOKEND PLAQUE TRUCK

Made in USA

Material: Wood and Metal

Length: 4½ inches

Notes: Bookend plaques available in gold and pewter, limited editions of five hundred each.

Value: Out of box (8 condition): $200

Mint condition in box: $325

1980s NOSTALGIC MINIATURE 1936 FORD V–8, PANEL TRUCK

Made in USA
Material: Die Cast
Length: 3¼ inches

Value: Out of box (8 condition): $80
Mint condition in box: $150

1980s NFIC BEDFORD FRICTION POWER DELIVERY TRUCK

Made in Hong Kong
Material: Plastic
Length: 6¼ inches
Notes: This friction power vehicle came with six strips of Coke cases.

Value: Out of box (8 condition): $100
Mint condition in box: $175

1980s NFIC FRICTION POWER BEDFORD DELIVERY TRUCK

Made in Hong Kong
Material: Plastic
Length: 6¼ inches
Notes: This Dinky-Toy copy was available in red and yellow and had six strips of cases on the back.

Value: Out of box (8 condition): $175
Mint condition in box: $250

1980s OLD CARS/GLAMOUR DELIVERY VAN

Made in Italy
Material: Die Cast
Scale: ¹⁄₄₃
Notes: There are two variations: Ineko and Fiat.

Value: Out of box (8 condition): $70
Mint condition in box: $100

● 1980s P.A.C. CHEVROLET COKE TRUCK

Made in USA
Material: Die Cast
Length: 3⅜ inches

Value: Out of box (8 condition): $35
Mint condition in box: $80

● 1980s REMCO TOYS INC. DELIVERY TRUCK SET

Made in China
Material: Steel
Length: 10¾ inches
Notes: This set included eight beverage cases, delivery truck and car, a vending machine and barriers. The Coca-Cola trailer had a door that opens.

Value: Out of box (8 condition): $20
Mint condition in box: $35

● 1980s SIKU EUROBUILT FORD BEVERAGE DELIVERY TRUCK

Made in West Germany
Material: Die Cast
Length: 7½ inches
Scale: ⅕₅

Value: Out of box (8 condition): $30
Mint condition in box: $55

● 1980s SIKU EUROBUILT MACK DELIVERY TRUCK

Made in West Germany

Material: Die Cast

Length: 12½ inches

Scale: ⅟₅₅

Notes: This truck is still fairly easy to find.

Value: Out of box (8 condition): $35
Mint condition in box: $55

● 1980s SIKU EUROBUILT MERCEDES STEP-IN DELIVERY VAN

Made in West Germany

Material: Die Cast

Length: 3½ inches

Scale: ⅟₅₅

Notes: This van has side and back doors that open.

Value: Out of box (8 condition): $35
Mint condition in box: $65

● 1980s SIKU EUROBUILT OLD-TIMER "A" FRAME DELIVERY TRUCK

Made in West Germany

Material: Die Cast

Length: 5¾ inches

Scale: ⅟₅₅

Notes: This scale reproduction of a 1934 delivery truck came with twelve cases and had elaborate detailing.

Value: Out of box (8 condition): $50
Mint condition in box: $80

● 1980s SOLIDO VW DELIVERY VAN

Made in France
Material: Die Cast
Scale: ¹/₄₃

Value: Out of box (8 condition): $20
Mint condition in box: $35

● 1980s STRACO ON POWER DELIVERY TRUCK

Made in Hong Kong
Material: Plastic
Length: 5 inches
Notes: This vehicle came with three different labels including Coca-Cola and Ice Cream.

Value: Out of box (8 condition): $30
Mint condition in box: $45

● 1980s SW (SUPER WHEELS) DELIVERY TRUCKS

Made in Hong Kong
Material: Die Cast
Length: 2³/₄ inches
Notes: These were available with different color cabs: white, yellow, brown, green, blue and red (the most common). Both the U.S. and Canadian versions are shown.

Value: Out of box (8 condition): $8
Mint condition in box: $20

● 1980s TIME WIND-UP DELIVERY TRUCK

Made in Japan
Material: Tin
Length: 3^5/$_{16}$ inches
Notes: This is a very difficult piece to find.

Value: Out of box (8 condition): $200
Mint condition in box: $275

● 1980s WAN DA TRACTOR TRAILER

Made in Taiwan
Material: Plastic
Length: 7½ inches

Value: Out of box (8 condition): $20
Mint condition in box: $30

● 1980s W.M./AGGLO FRICTION POWER DELIVERY TRUCK

Made in Japan (WM), Hong Kong (Agglo)
Material: Tin
Length: 3¾ inches
Notes: The red cab variation made in Hong Kong is much rarer than the others and is valued from $80 to $100.

Value: Out of box (8 condition): $10
Mint condition in box: $35

● 1980s W.M. SUPER MINI SERIES FRICTION POWER TRUCK SET

Made in Japan, Taiwan, Hong Kong
Material: Tin
Length: 1½ inches
Notes: Individual trucks are valued from $10–20.

Value: Out of box (8 condition): $100
Mint condition in box: $175

● 1980 S YATMING ON-POWER DELIVERY VAN

Made in China
Material: Die Cast and Plastic
Length: 2¾ inches
Notes: These trucks were available in five different colors.

Value: Out of box (8 condition): $10
Mint condition in box: $20

● 1981 BUDDY L BRUTE TRAILER
Made in USA
Material: Steel
Length: 10³⁄₄ inches
Notes: This truck's trailer came with five red cases and one hand truck.

Value: Out of box (8 condition): $25
Mint condition in box: $45

● 1981 BUDDY L DELIVERY TRUCK
Made in Japan
Material: Steel
Length: 4³⁄₄ inches
Notes: This truck came with one case of bottles.

Value: Out of box (8 condition): $35
Mint condition in box: $65

● 1983 NOSTALGIC MINIATURE COKE TRUCK CAB
Made in USA
Material: Die Cast
Length: 4³⁄₄ inches

Value: Out of box (8 condition): $80
Mint condition in box: $125

● 1985 SMITH TRACTOR TRAILER

Made in England
Material: Die Cast
Notes: These Smith Mack trucks were hand-built in England in the 1980s. They had a very limited production and were finely detailed.

Value: Out of box (8 condition): $200
Mint condition in box: $350

● 1986 HAROLD FORD METALCRAFT DELIVERY TRUCK

Made in USA
Material: Wood
Length: 10¾ inches
Notes: Harold Ford carved only ten of these trucks. Harold lives is Louisville, Kentucky and carves wood toys in small quantities but with wonderful quality.

Value: Out of box (8 condition): $350
Mint condition in box: $450

● 1986 TOMICA ISUZU TRUCK

Made in Japan
Material: Die Cast
Scale: 1/70
Notes: This was a Coca-Cola 100th Anniversary Isuzu truck.

Value: Out of box (8 condition): $100
Mint condition in box: $150

● 1990s DELIVERY TRUCKS

Made in Hong Kong

Material: Die Cast

Length: 4 inches each

Notes: These trucks came in green, red and yellow.

Value: Out of box (8 condition): $25 each

Mint condition in box: $35 each

● 1990s LIEDO 1928 CHEVROLET DELIVERY VEHICLE

Made in England

Material: Die Cast

Length: 3 inches

Value: Out of box (8 condition): $10

Mint condition in box: $20

● 1990s LIEDO 1937 SCAMMELL SIX WHEELER

Made in England

Material: Die Cast

Length: 4¼ inches

Value: Out of box (8 condition): $10

Mint condition in box: $25

● 1990s LIEDO DAYS GONE 1938 CHEVY PICKUP TRUCK

Made in England
Material: Die Cast
Length: 3¼ inches

Value: Out of box (8 condition): $15
Mint condition in box: $25

● 1990s LIEDO 1942 DODGE 4X4 DELIVERY VEHICLE

Made in England
Material: Die Cast
Length: 3¼ inches

Value: Out of box (8 condition): $15
Mint condition in box: $25

● 1990s MAJORETTE TRACTOR TRAILER AND CARS

Material: Plastic and Die Cast
Length: 6 inches (truck)

Value: Out of box (8 condition): $5
Mint condition in box: $10

● 1990s SOLIDO RENAULT ESPACE

Made in France
Material: Die Cast
Scale: 1/43

Value: Out of box (8 condition): $20
Mint condition in box: $35

● 1990s TOMY DELIVERY TRUCK SET

Made in Japan
Material: Die Cast
Length: 3 inches each

Value: Out of box (8 condition): $20 (set of four)
Mint condition in box: $35 (set of four)

● 1990 TOMY COCA-COLA EVENT TRUCK #37

Made in Japan
Material: Die Cast and Plastic
Length: 3 inches

Value: Out of box (8 condition): $8
Mint condition in box: $15

● 1991 CE DELIVERY TRUCKS

Made in Hong Kong
Material: Plastic and
Die Cast
Length: 3¾ inches
Notes: The set
of six is worth
$135.

*Value: Out of
box (8 condi-
tion): $25
Mint condition
in box: $35*

● 1995 MAJOREM COCA-COLA JEEP

Material: Die Cast
Length: 3¼ inches

*Value: Out of box
(8 condition): $2
Mint condition in
box: $5*

● 1996 LIEDO DAYS GONE ATLANTA 1996 OLYMPIC COKE TRUCK

Made in England
Material: Die Cast
Length: 3 inches
Notes: This truck was produced for the
Atlanta Committee for the Olympic
Games — 1928–1996.

*Value: Out of box (8 condition):
$10
Mint condition in box: $20*

1998 WINROSS COCA-COLA TRACTOR TRAILER

Made in USA
Material: Die Cast
Length: 13¼ inches
Notes: This limited
release Coca-Cola truck was made for the 24th Annual 1998 Coca-Cola Collectors Club Convention held in Minneapolis, Minnesota.

Value: Out of box (8 condition): $65
Mint condition in box: $125

1999 LIMITED EDITION HOLIDAY CLASSIC CARRIER TRUCK

Material: Plastic
Length: 15 inches
Notes: This truck had battery-operated lights and a detachable cab and trailer. It also included a 1953 Corvette on the trailer.

Value: Out of box (8 condition): $15
Mint condition in box: $25

1990s MATCHBOX 1912 FORD MODEL T TRUCK

Material: Die Cast
Length: 3½ inches
Notes: Written on the side of the truck is, "Ice Cold Coca-Cola Sold Here."

Value: Out of box (8 condition): $10
Mint condition in box: $25

• 1990s MATCHBOX COLLECTIBLES 1921 MODEL T FORD

Material: Die Cast

Scale: 1/64

*Value: Out of box
(8 condition): $5
Mint condition in box: $10*

• 1990s MATCHBOX 1930 MODEL A PICKUP TRUCK

Material: Die Cast

Length: 4 inches

Notes: This Models of Yesteryear 1930 Model A truck has gold wheels. Written on the side of the truck is, "Parts and Maintenance, Atlanta Bottling Company, Atlanta, Georgia."

*Value: Out of box (8 condition): $10
Mint condition in box: $25*

• 1990s MATCHBOX 1932 FORD AA DELIVERY TRUCK

Material: Die Cast

Length: 4¼ inches

Notes: This Models of Yesteryear 1932 Ford AA delivery truck, has written on the side, "Delicious, Coca-Cola, Refreshing, Coca-Cola Bottling Company, Atlanta Georgia."

*Value: Out of box (8 condition): $10
Mint condition in box: $25*

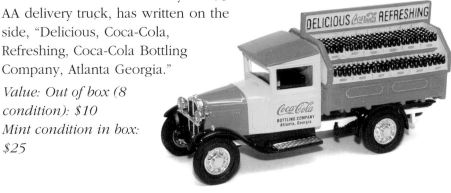

● 1990s MATCHBOX 1957 CHEVY PICKUP TRUCK

Material: Die Cast

Length: 4½ inches

Scale: ⅟₄₃

Value: Out of box (8 condition): $15

Mint condition in box: $45

● 1990s MATCHBOX 1955 FORD F-100 PICKUP TRUCK

Material: Die Cast

Length: 4½ inches

Notes: This 1955 Ford F–100 pickup has, "Pause and Refresh, " written on the front fender.

Value: Out of box (8 condition): $10

Mint condition in box: $20

● 1990s MATCHBOX 1937 GMC DELIVERY VEHICLE

Material: Die Cast

Length: 4¼ inches

Notes: This Models of Yesteryear vehicle has, "Special Delivery, " written on the door.

Value: Out of box (8 condition): $10

Mint condition in box: $25

Coca-Cola Archive Images

This gallery of Coca-Cola Archive photos shows Coca-Cola delivery vehicles as they have appeared through the years. The toy trucks have often mirrored the working versions, which represent the history of The Coca-Cola Company and society in general.

1900s

1900s

1913 — *Truck decorated for a parade in Shreveport, Louisiana*

1922 — Greenville, South Carolina

1925

1926 — New Orleans

1928 – Studebaker in Tampa, Florida

1928

1920s

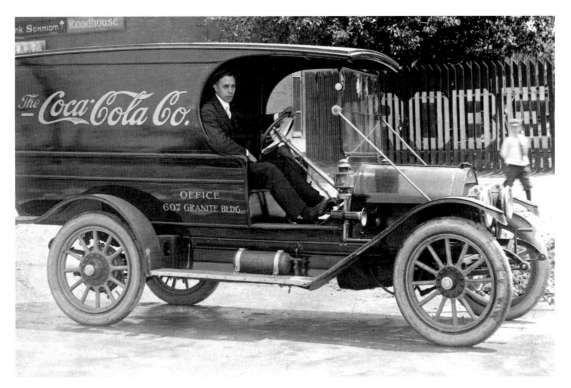

1920s

1938 – A.S. Wilson delivery truck in Scotland

CHAPTER 2

Coca-Cola
Cars

1918 Company car – New Orleans

S ome collectors may find hunting down replicas of antique Coca-Cola delivery vehicles a bit stodgy. And that's where Coca-Cola cars carve their niche.

Instead of capturing precious moments in time, Coca-Cola cars are more a reflection of the times. Whereas Coca-Cola trucks show Coca-Cola history, the cars show how Coke fits into the American way of life.

The majority of Coca-Cola cars, from hot rods to taxis to VW Beetles, have been manufactured within the past thirty years. Many of the same companies that manufacture the Coke trucks—Matchbox, Taiyo, Corgi and Buddy L—also make Coca-Cola cars.

A large portion of Coca-Cola cars are racecars, especially when you include the large number of NASCAR Coca-Cola die cast that is now being produced. Remote control Coke cars have also been very popular.

1920 advertising car – Tampa, Florida

1938 salesman's car

1941 salesman's car

1962 promotional wagon – Danville, Virginia

Coca-Cola Cars

● 1954, 1956 TAIYO SPEED JACK HOT ROD
Made in Japan
Material: Tin and Plastic
Length: 10¼ inches
Notes: This battery-operated
Bump 'N Go Action Hot
Rod came in two varia-
tions: the Snake and the
Mongoose.

Value: Out of box (8 condition): $80
Mint condition in box: $175

● 1960s TAIYO FRICTION POWER FORD TAXI
Made in Japan
Material: Tin
Length: 9 inches

Value: Out of box (8 condition): $300
Mint condition in box: $400

● 1960s TAIYO FRICTION POWER FORD ZEST CAR
Made in Japan
Material: Tin
Length: 9 inches
Notes: There were two
variations of this car:
one with chrome
wheels and one with
white wheels. This car
also came in both a blue box and a red box.

Value: Out of box (8 condition): $250
Mint condition in box: $375

● 1970s MATTEL HOT WHEELS CARS
Made in USA
Material: Die Cast
Length: 3 inches
Notes: The Coca-Cola Hot Wheels came in two different models

(Mongoose and Snake) and in four different color variations (blue, yellow, white and red). The Coca-Cola Red Line Hot Wheels have red wall tires, making them the most collectible for the Hot Wheels collector.

Value: Out of box (8 condition): $60 Mint condition in box: $150

● 1970s TAIYO RUSHER SNAKE II CORVETTE STINGRAY

Made in Japan
Material: Tin
Length: 7½ inches
Notes: This is a Bump 'N Go battery operated car with lights that can blink. A Mongoose model was never made of this car.

Value: Out of box (8 condition): $65
Mint condition in box: $150

● 1970 CORGI TURBO RACING TEAM TRUCK, TRAILER AND CAR

Made in Great Britain
Material: Die Cast
Length: 10½ inches

Value: Out of box (8 condition): $30
Mint condition in box: $65

● 1971–1994 BUDDY L POP ART BUGGIES SET #4999

Made in Japan
Material: Steel and Plastic
Length: 2½ inches each
Notes: The individual Coke
car is valued at $85. The Pop Art Buggies came in a set of four, with these available vehicles: Coca-Cola, Lightbulb, Skippy Peanut Butter, Heinz, Kellogg's, and Bazooka Gum. These vehicles were made to Buddy L's specifications in Japan.

Value: Out of box (8 condition): $300 (set)
Mint condition in box:
$400 (set)

● 1979 CORGI TURBO RACING TEAM SET

Made in Great Britain
Material: Die Cast
Length: 2¾ inches
Notes: The Coca-Cola Racing Team included three vehicles: a hot rod custom van, Chevrolet Corvette and a Pontiac Firebird.

Value: Out of box (8 condition): $15 (set)
Mint condition in box: $35 (set)

● 1980S ASAHI MYSTERY ACTION VW DERBY RALLY CAR

Made in Japan
Material: Tin
Length: 8¾ inches
Notes: Battery operated car.

Value: Out of box (8 condition): $225
Mint condition in box: $375

● 1980s BURAGO COCA-COLA CAR
Made in Italy
Material: Die Cast
Scale: 1/43

Value: Out of box (8 condition): $15
Mint condition in box: $25

● 1980s TAIYO/GALOOB REMOTE CONTROL CORVETTE STINGRAY
Made in Japan
Material: Plastic
Length: 8 inches

Value: Out of box (8 condition): $40
Mint condition in box: $50

● 1980s TYCO RACE CAR
Made in Singapore
Material: Plastic
Length: 10 inches

Value: Out of box (8 condition): $25
Mint condition in box: $35

● 1980s TYCO SLOT CAR
Made in Singapore
Material: Resin Composite
Length: 3 1/8 inches

Value: Out of box (8 condition): $40
Mint condition in box: $60

● 1980s VITESSE PORSCHE 956

Made in Portugal
Material: Die Cast
Scale: $^1/_{43}$

Value: Out of box (8 condition): $50
Mint condition in box: $70

● 1980 FRICTION POWER RACE CARS

Made in Japan
Material: Tin
Length: 5$^1/_4$ inches
Notes: Six different cars
in each set, only two are
Coca-Cola cars.

*Value: Out of box (8
condition): $25*
Mint condition in box: $35

● 1980 HARD TOYS MICRO CARS

Material: Plastic
Length: 1$^1/_4$ inches

*Value: Out of box (8
condition): $7*
Mint condition in box: $12

● 1990s MAJORETTE TRACTOR TRAILER AND CARS

Material: Plastic and Die Cast
Length: 6 inches (truck)

*Value: Out of
box (8 con-
dition): $5*
*Mint condi-
tion in box:
$10*

1990s MATCHBOX COLLECTIBLES 1962 VW BEETLE

Material: Die Cast
Length: 3 inches

Value: Out of box (8 condition): $5
Mint condition in box: $10

1990s PULL BACK BUMP 'N GO RACE CARS

Made in USA
Material: Plastic
Length: 2¾ inches
Notes: Sprite, Diet Coke and Fanta race cars.

Value: Out of box (8 condition): $20
Mint condition in box: $30

1990 ONYX MODEL CARS—RACE CAR

Made in Portugal
Material: Die Cast
Length: 4 inches

Value: Out of box (8 condition): $25
Mint condition in box: $45

1994 EDOCAR/EDOR VW BUG CAR

Made in the Netherlands
Material: Die Cast
Length: 2½ inches

Value: Out of box (8 condition): $5
Mint condition in box: $10

● **1998 TYCO REMOTE CONTROL TARGET FORMULA ONE RACE CAR**

Material: Plastic

Length: 12½ inches

Value: Out of box (8 condition): $15
Mint condition in box: $45

● **1999 TYCO CANNED HEAT REMOTE CONTROL CAR**

Material: Plastic with Metal Wheels

Length: 5¾ inches

Notes: This is a 1957 Chevrolet remote control car.

Value: Out of box (8 condition): $10
Mint condition in box: $20

1970s race car

CHAPTER 3

Coca-Cola and NASCAR

Dale Earnhardt Sr. and Jr. at the NASCAR Thunder Special Motegi Coca-Cola 500

NASCAR and Coca-Cola have always been the perfect teammates. Coke arguably owns the most recognizable trademarks on Earth and NASCAR and its drivers are inextricably linked to their sponsors. For thirty years, Coca-Cola has been connected with NASCAR, and their bond has grown stronger in recent years.

When it comes to collectible cars and trucks, Coca-Cola has been involved for more than a century. NASCAR and its brightly painted vehicles make a perfect canvas for the Coca-Cola trademark and logo. And as this relationship grows, so should the opportunities for Coca-Cola car and truck collectors.

The Coca-Cola brand "Mello Yello" sponsored Kyle Petty for a number of years, making for a very popular pairing. Die-cast cars and other collectibles were made of his lime-green and black Mello Yello paint scheme.

The NASCAR Thunder Special Motegi Coca-Cola 500, held in Motegi City, Japan on November 22, 1998, is the inspiration behind a number of collectibles featuring Dale Earnhardt Jr. and the Coke polar bear car logo.

The Coca-Cola Company also sponsored the legendary Bobby Allison and his NASCAR team.

The Company's involvement as a NASCAR sponsor has increased in recent years, but Coca-Cola became a huge player in 1998 by becoming the "Official Soft Drink of NASCAR." For more than a decade, Coca-Cola has sponsored NASCAR's Memorial Day weekend race, the Coca-Cola 600, in Charlotte, North Carolina, at Charlotte Motor Speedway. Licensed event collectibles, from die-cast vehicles to racing jackets to trading cards and caps, are created for each Coca-Cola sponsored race.

1998 Coca-Cola 300 winner, Dale Earnhardt Jr.

Coca-Cola also created the Coca-Cola Racing Family, a group of the top NASCAR drivers affiliated with the soft drink giant. The Racing Family includes Jeff Burton, Dale Earnhardt Sr., Dale Earnhardt Jr., Kenny Irwin, Dale Jarrett, Bobby Labonte, Jeremy Mayfield, Steve Park, Kyle Petty, Ricky Rudd, and Tony Stewart. Coca-Cola also sponsors the "Coca-Cola Wall of Speed," a NASCAR driving simulator in which fans can match their times against drivers in the Coca-Cola Racing Family.

An important day in NASCAR and Coca-Cola racing history occurred on November 22, 1998, in Motegi City, Japan. Dale Earnhardt Sr. and Jr. raced against each other for the first time during the NASCAR Thunder Special Motegi Coca-Cola 500. Both drove Chevrolets sporting special paint schemes. Dale Earnhardt Jr. drove a black Monte Carlo featuring on its hood a Coca-Cola Polar Bear drinking a Coke, while his father's No. 3 car was painted bright red with the Coca-Cola Racing Family logo on the hood. This event resulted in the most, and some of the best, Coca-Cola die-casts and other collectibles.

We've included a sampling of Coca-Cola NASCAR collectibles in this chapter, including die-cast cars, trucks and banks. Available Coca-Cola NASCAR licensed items should grow exponentially in the next few years and will continue to combine these two giants and their collectors.

Coca-Cola and NASCAR

● **1993–1995 ACTION/RCCA KYLE PETTY MELLO YELLO CAR**

Paint Scheme: Mello Yello

Scale: 1/64

Notes: This car was made by Action but distributed through its club (RCCA). The hood of this car opens.

Value: Near Mint: $5.50
Mint: $12

● **1995 AMERICAN PLASTIC TOYS INC. BILL ELLIOTT CAR**

Made in USA

Material: Plastic

Length: 15¾ inches

Value: Out of box (8 condition): $10
Mint condition in box: $25

● **1995 RACING CHAMPIONS COCA-COLA 600 TRUCK SERIES BANK**

Made in China

Material: Die Cast

Scale: 1/24

Notes: This coin bank with key is a die cast from the Coca-Cola 600 —Super Truck Series at Charlotte Motor Speedway.

Value: Out of box (8 condition): $35
Mint condition in box: $45

● **1995 RACING CHAMPIONS COCA-COLA 600 BANK**

Made in China

Material: Die Cast

Scale: ¹/₂₄

Notes: This is a Charlotte Motor Speedway Coca-Cola 600 bank.

Value: Out of box (8 condition): $45
Mint condition in box: $65

● **1997 REVELL RACING COCA-COLA 600 MONTE CARLO**

Made in England

Material: Die Cast

Scale: ¹/₆₄

Notes: This die cast commemorates NASCAR's Coca-Cola 600, held at Charlotte Motor Speedway.

Value: Out of box (8 condition): $2
Mint condition in box: $5

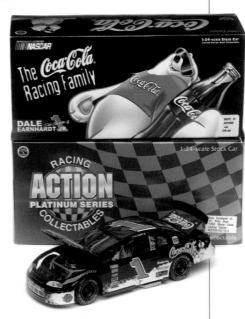

● **1998 ACTION RACING COLLECTIBLES DALE EARNHARDT JR. COKE CAR**

Paint Scheme: #1 Polar Bear Coke

Scale: ¹/₂₄

Value: Near Mint: $32
Mint: $70

● **1998 ACTION RACING COLLECTIBLES DALE EARNHARDT COKE CAR**

Paint Scheme: #3 Coca-Cola Racing Family

Scale: ¹/₂₄

Value: Near Mint: $29
Mint: $65

● 1998 ACTION RACING COLLECTIBLES DALE EARNHARDT JR. COKE CAR

Paint Scheme: #1 Polar Bear Coke
Scale: 1/64

Value: Near Mint: $6.75
Mint: $15

● 1998 ACTION/RCCA DALE EARNHARDT JR. COKE CAR

Paint Scheme: #1 Polar Bear
Coke
Scale: 1/64
Notes: This car was made by
Action but distributed through its club (RCCA). The hood of this car
opens.

Value: Near Mint: $13.50
Mint: $30

● 1998 ACTION/RCCA DALE EARNHARDT COKE CAR

Paint Scheme: #3 Coca-Cola Racing Family
Scale: 1/64
Notes: This car was made by Action but distributed through its club
(RCCA). The hood
of this car opens.

Value: Near Mint:
$13.50
Mint: $30

● 1998 WINNER'S CIRCLE EARNHARDT JR. AND EARNHARDT SR. COKE CARS

Paint Schemes:
Earnhardt Jr.—#1 black car with Coke polar bear on hood.
Earnhardt Sr.—#3 red car with the Coca-Cola Racing Family logo on hood.
Material: Die Cast
Scale: 1/43

Value: Out of box
(8 condition): $10 (each)
Mint condition in box: $25 (each)

● 1998-1999 ACTION PERFORMANCE DALE EARNHARDT JR. GAS PUMP

Scale: 1/64
Material: Die Cast
Notes: Limited to 6,000.

Value: Out of box (8 condition): $10

Mint condition in box: $20

● 1999 WINNERS CIRCLE EARNHARDT JR. PIT ROW

Made in England
Material: Die Cast
Scale: 1/64

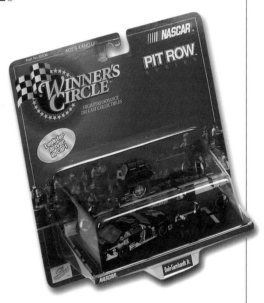

Notes: This train has six pieces: an engine, caboose, coal car, box car, car transporter and race car.

Value: Out of box (8 condition): $20

Mint condition in box: $30

CHAPTER 4

Coca-Cola Trains and Buses

1928 – Trolley on the streets of Barcelona, Spain

T he toy train has always been a child's dream Christmas gift, and the holidays and Coke have long gone together.

Remember the advertisement featuring Santa Claus standing in front of a Christmas tree, drinking a Coke with a toy train running around his boots? These toy vehicles hail from Germany, Japan, Austria, Italy and the United States and their values can range from less than twenty dollars to more than a thousand dollars. Unlike the Coca-Cola cars and trucks, there were not many Coke buses or trains produced.

Even prior to the 1970s there were very few Coca-Cola trains to collect, but there was a very rare and beautiful train made about 1928, the American Flyer "Pure as Sunlight" Train, which serves as one of the earliest known and most valuable locomotives.

During the 1970s a number of very detailed, high-quality trains entered the market. Most of these were made of plastic instead of tin,

1936 advertisement

which some collectors prefer. But the supply of available trains and buses continues to grow for the collector.

With trains and buses there aren't as many collectibles to choose from, making the hunt all the more exciting.

1962 advertisement

Coca-Cola Trains and Buses

● **1928–1930 AMERICAN FLYER "PURE AS SUNLIGHT" TRAIN PASSENGER CAR**

Made in USA

Material: Tin

Notes: This is one car from a set that included: one locomotive, one tender, one baggage car, two passenger cars and eight pieces of track. The train was a wind-up powered and the value of the complete set is $8,500. This is one of the most difficult Coca-Cola toys to find and very little is known about the history of this train. The "Pure as Sunlight" slogan was used by Coca-Cola from the late 1920s to the early 1930s.

Value: Out of box (8 condition): $1,500
Mint condition in box: $1,850

● **1950s TECHNOFIX WIND-UP BUS**

Made in West Germany

Material: Tin

Length: 40 inches

Notes: This is a wind-up bus and terminal. For one version of this bus terminal the key cannot be removed, that version is the newest and most rare.

Value: Out of box (8 condition): $350
Mint condition in box: $500

● 1950s ANGUPLAS
DOUBLE DECKER BUS

Made in Spain
Material: Plastic
Length: 3 inches

Value: Out of box (8 condition): $125

Mint condition in box: $200

● 1956 AMOLD SPIELWAREN WIND-UP TRAIN

Made in West Germany
Material: Tin
Length: 14 inches
Notes: This toy is very difficult to find. It came in two box variations, no difference in the train.

Value: Out of box (8 condition): $500
Mint condition in box: $750

● 1960 COCA-COLA WIND-UP FREIGHT TRAIN

Made in Japan
Material: Tin
Length: 16½ inches (each car—2½ inches)

Value: Out of box
(8 condition): $500
Mint condition in box: $650

● 1970s ATHEARN
COCA-COLA TRAIN CAR

Made in USA
Material: Plastic
Scale: HO

Value: Out of box (8 condition):
$20
Mint condition in box: $35

● 1970s PAYVA TRANVIA
FRICTION POWER
TRAIN

Made in Spain
Material: Plastic
Length: 7 inches

Value: Out of box
(8 condition): $125
Mint condition in box: $200

● 1970s S.T. "WELCOME TO JAPAN" DOUBLE-DECKER BUS

Made in Japan
Material: Tin
Length: 17¾ inches
Notes: This friction power
double-decker bus was not
available in the United States.

Value: Out of box (8 condi-
tion): $300
Mint condition in box: $450

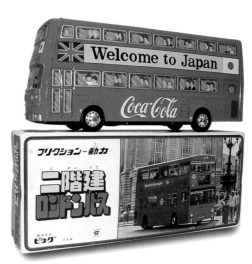

● 1970 BERTREN COCA-COLA TRAIN CAR

Made in Germany
Material: Plastic
Length: 2½ inches
Scale: HO

Value: Out of box (8 condition): $25
Mint condition in box: $50

● 1970 LILIPUT MODELLBAHN TRAIN CAR

Made in Austria
Material: Plastic
Length: 4 inches

Value: Out of box (8 condition): $20
Mint condition in box: $50

● 1973 LIONEL COCA-COLA TRAIN SET

Made in USA
Material: Metal and Plastic
Scale: 027 Gage
Notes: This train had working headlights on the engine and had three box cars: Sprite (green), Tab (red) and Fanta (orange). It also came with a Coca-Cola caboose. There were two versions of this train set: the version shown and the Chattanooga seventy-fifth anniversary version made in 1974. The Chattanooga version is worth twenty-five percent more.

Value: Out of box (8 condition): $250
Mint condition in box: $650

● 1980s FLEISCHMANN TRAIN

Made in Germany
Material: Plastic
Length: 4 inches

Value: Out of box (8 condition): $30 Mint condition in box: $50

● 1980s K-LINE
COCA-COLA FLAT BED TRAIN CAR

Material: Plastic
Length: 9½ inches

Value: Out of box (8 condition): $20 Mint condition in box: $35

● 1980s LIMA TRAIN #152301

Made in Italy
Material: Plastic
Length: 2¾ inches
Notes: This is a battery operated, boxed set of four.

Value: Out of box (8 condition): $60 Mint condition in box: $100

● 1991 K-LINE COCA-COLA SANTA TRAIN CAR

Material: Plastic

Length: 9½ inches

*Value: Out of box
(8 condition): $20
Mint condition in box:
$50*

● 1999 REVELL DALE
EARNHARDT JR. TRAIN SET

Made in England

Scale: HO

Notes: This train has six pieces: an engine, caboose, coal car, box car, car transporter and race car.

Value: Out of box (8 condition): $20

*Mint condition
in box: $30*

CHAPTER 5

Coca-Cola Banks

1940s – San Antonio, Texas

These aren't your standard ceramic pigs. Coca-Cola banks come in all types, shapes and sizes, from plastic to die cast, from Coke machines to NASCAR racecars.

One of the early, and most interesting, Coca-Cola banks was the battery-operated 1950s Louis Marx dispenser bank with lights. This Coca-Cola dispenser bank came with four glasses and was manufactured by the Louis Marx Company. It was made of tin and its presentation box was adorned with a picture of the bank inside.

There were several different types of plastic banks produced in the 1950s, and some included the additional feature of dispensing miniature bottles of Coke with each deposit.

During the 1990s, Ertl produced numerous die cast metal Coca-Cola airplanes, automobiles and trucks that also just happened to serve as banks. With The Coca-Cola Company becoming a much larger sponsor of NASCAR, the number of die cast collectible banks naturally increased. Coke has created die cast collectibles of the races it sponsors, including the Coca-Cola 600. Racing Champions and Ertl both make die cast replicas of NASCAR cars sporting Coca-Cola paint schemes.

Around the turn of the century, there has been a bonanza of new entries into this secondary collecting field. Companies such as Enesco are producing superior products, including banks that are made in the form of old-fashioned soda machines or juke boxes that play music each time a coin is added. Some of these recordings (including, of course, "I'd Like to Buy the World a Coke") strive to remind us of our youth—and succeed.

Coca-Cola Banks

● 1950s LOUIS MARX CO. DISPENSER BANK

Made in USA
Material: Tin
Height: 9¾ inches
Notes: This bank was available in two different boxes. It came with three glasses, was battery operated and had lights that could be turned on.

Value: Out of box (8 condition): $550
Mint condition in box: $900

● 1960s VENDING MACHINE BANK

Made in USA
Material: Plastic
Height: 5½ inches
Notes: This bank dispenses small bottles of Coca-Cola.

Value: Out of box (8 condition): $45
Mint condition in box: $60

● 1960 COCA-COLA BANK

Made in Mexico
Material: Pressed Steel
Size: 9 inches by 5 inches by 5 inches

Value: Out of box (8 condition): $300
Mint condition in box: $800

● 1980 MSR IMPORTS VENDING MACHINE BANK

Made in Hong Kong
Material: Plastic
Size: 6½ x 3 inches

Value: Out of box (8 condition): $30

Mint condition in box: $50

● 1990s ERTL 1930 CHEVROLET TRUCK BANK

Material: Die Cast
Length: 3½ inches
Notes: This Ertl truck bank has, "Ask Your Dealer," written on the door.

Value: Out of box (8 condition): $10
Mint condition in box: $25

● 1995 RACING CHAMPIONS COCA-COLA 600 BANK

Made in China
Material: Die Cast
Scale: ¹/₂₄
Notes: This is a Charlotte Motor Speedway Coca-Cola 600 bank.

Value: Out of box (8 condition): $45
Mint condition in box: $65

● 1995 RACING CHAMPIONS COCA-COLA 600 TRUCK SERIES BANK

Made in China
Material: Die Cast
Scale: $^{1}/_{24}$
Notes: This coin bank with key is a die cast from the Coca-Cola 600—Super Truck Series at Charlotte Motor Speedway.

Value: Out of box (8 condition): $40
Mint condition in box: $60

1997 ERTL STEARMAN BI-PLANE BANK

Made in USA
Material: Die Cast
Scale: 1/43

Value: Out of box (8 condition): $20

Mint condition in box: $30

• 1999 ERTL 1931 STEARMAN REPLICA AIRPLANE BANK #19582

Made in England

Material: Die Cast

Notes: This authentic 1931 Stearman replica Coca-Cola metal bank was available at the Coca-Cola Collectors Club 25th Annual Convention, August 8–14, 1999 in Dallas, Texas.

Value: Out of box (8 condition): $30
Mint condition in box: $50

CHAPTER 6

Coca-Cola Miscellaneous

1970 – Milan, Italy

1930 – Fokker Trimotor airplane at Atlanta Airport

Coca-Cola collecting isn't limited to trucks, cars, trains and buses. Airplanes, models, remote control robots and even a radiator plate from a 1920 Coke delivery truck are all fair game for the Coca-Cola car and truck collector.

There are hundreds, possibly thousands, of items emblazoned with images of Coke delivery trucks and cars. Show your allegiance with a set of playing cards, a matchbox, or even a Coke license plate.

Miniature Coke bottles and toy car accessories, including handcarts, have become collectibles themselves. These items came with Coca-Cola delivery truck toys and are often very intricate and unusual, making them interesting collectibles. The Coke trucks have a much higher value when all of the accessories are intact, but the cases of bottles and handcarts have been easily lost or damaged through the years.

These miscellaneous Coke vehicle items can be fun to collect and add variety to any Coca-Cola trucks and cars collection.

Truck on the square at the clock tower in London

Egypt

Coca-Cola Miscellaneous

● **1920 BROWN MANUFACTURING RADIATOR PLATE FOR COCA-COLA TRUCK**

Made in USA
Material: Cast Aluminum
Length: 17 inches
Notes: Beware of reproductions.

Value: 8 condition: $550
Mint condition: $675

● **1950 SCHUCO ESPRESSO CAFÉ AND SNACK BAR**

Made in Germany
Material: Tin and Plastic
Length: 8 inches

Value: Out of box (8 condition): $150
Mint condition in box: $250

● **1960s DISPLAY CORPORATION RACE CAR WALL PLAQUE**

Made in USA
Material: Plastic
Size: 15½ inches by 16½ inches
Notes: This is an international road race 3-D cutout. It was in a set of four race car signs.

Value: 8 condition: $125
Mint condition: $225

● 1970s COCA-COLA LICENSE PLATE

Material: Tin
Size: 11¾ inches by 6 inches

Value: 8 condition: $5
Mint condition: $15

● 1970s TIGER CUTOUTS COCA-COLA AIRPLANE

Made in USA
Material: Styrofoam
Size: 7 inches by 5½ inches

Value: Out of box (8 condition): $5
Mint condition in box: $10

● 1977–1979 CC TRADING CO. COBOT REMOTE CONTROL ROBOT

Made in Korea
Material: Plastic
Height: 9 inches

Value: Out of box (8 condition): $85
Mint condition in box: $200

● 1980s TOMY REMOTE CONTROL ROBOT

Made in Japan
Material: Plastic
Height: 9 inches

Value: Out of box (8 condition): $200
Mint condition in box: $375

● 1990s AMT 1957 CHEVROLET MODEL KIT

Made in USA
Material: Plastic
Scale: ¹/₂₅

Value: Out of box (8 condition): $10
Mint condition in box: $15

● 1992 COCA-COLA DELIVERY TRUCK PLAYING CARDS

Notes: These cards were given away at the Sixteenth Annual Septemberfest, E-Town, Kentucky, September 17–19, 1992

Value: Out of box (8 condition): $10

Mint condition in box: $12

● COCA-COLA MATCH BOX WITH TRUCK IMAGE

Size: 2³⁄₈ inches by 1⁷⁄₈ inches

Value: Mint condition: $4

● 1995 BRISTOLWARE COKE DELIVERY TRUCK COOKIE TIN

Material: Tin
Length: 7 inches

Value: Out of box (8 condition): $5
Mint condition in box: $10

Mini-Bottles

● 1930s CASE OF MINI COCA-COLA BOTTLES

Size: 3³⁄₄ inches by 2³⁄₄ inches
Notes: This case of twelve bottles each is 2¹⁄₂ inches high. Two different companies manufactured these bottles; their marks are on the bottom of the bottles. Chattanooga Glass–identified by a "C" within a circle and Owens Illinois–identified by an "I" printed over an "O" surrounded by a diamond.

Value: 8 condition: $100
Mint condition: $175

● 1934 OWENS CUBAN MINI COKE BOTTLES

Size: 6¼ inches by 4¼ inches (case)

Notes: These Coca-Cola bottles were sent to Cuba. Two different companies manufactured these bottles; their marks are on the bottom of the bottles. The manufacturers are

Chattanooga Glass, identified by a "C" within a circle, and Owens Illinois, identified by an "I" printed over an "O" surrounded by a diamond.

Value: 8 condition: $150
Mint condition: $250

● 1954 AND 1979 MINI COKE BOTTLES

Notes: The deep-etched case with light green bottles are from 1954. The stenciled cases with the dark green bottles are from 1979. They were both used on the Smith-Miller Coca-Cola truck.

Light Green Case

Value: 8 condition: $10
Mint condition: $20

Dark Green Case

Value: 8 condition: $35
Mint condition: $40

● **Cases of bottles and push trucks that came with the Coca-Cola toy trucks as accessories.**

Printed Material

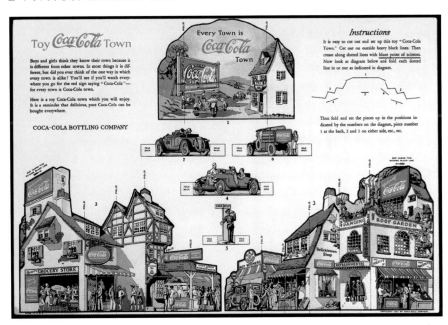

● **1927 COCA-COLA CUTOUT**

Material: Cardboard

Value: 8 condition: $4,500

Mint condition: $6,000

1929 OVERSEAS EDITION OF *THE RED BARREL*

Notes: March edition with Coke truck and the Coliseum on the cover.

Value: 8 condition: $65
Mint condition: $90

1930 COCA-COLA PRINT ADVERTISEMENT

Notes Coke truck is shown in Genoa, Italy.

Value: 8 condition: $50
Mint condition: $60

● 1954 COCA-COLA OVERSEAS

Notes: February edition with Coke truck crossing a canal in Holland on the cover.

Value: 8 condition: $10

Mint condition: $18

● 1955 COCA-COLA OVERSEAS

Notes: June edition with Coke truck on a Paris street on the cover.

Value: 8 condition: $10

Mint condition: $18

● 1956 COCA-COLA OVERSEAS

Notes: June edition with Coke truck in Valduz, Liechtenstein on the cover.

Value: 8 condition: $10

Mint condition: $18

● 1960 COCA-COLA OVERSEAS

Notes: October edition with Coke truck parked in front of the United Nations building on the cover.

Value: 8 condition: $8

Mint condition: $12

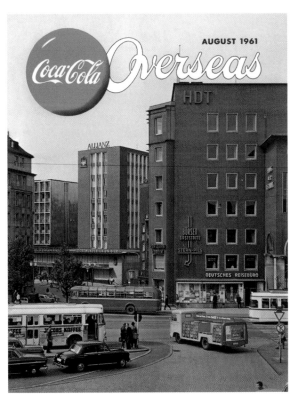

AUGUST 1961

Coca-Cola *Overseas*

● **1961 COCA-COLA OVERSEAS**

Notes: August edition with Coke truck in Essen, Germany on the cover.

Value: 8 condition: $8

Mint condition: $12

NOVEMBER 1989

● **1989 COKE CALENDAR — NOVEMBER**

Notes: "Can't Beat the Feeling."

Value: 8 condition: $5

Mint condition: $7

CHAPTER 7

Maintaining Coca-Cola Cars and Trucks

Model 3022T Tractor-Trailer in Clarksburg, West Virginia

*Collectors have many options for storing,
displaying, protecting, restoring and even
insuring their Coke cars and trucks*

Collecting Coca-Cola cars and trucks can be addictive.

Before you know it, those first few trucks have turned into an ever-growing fleet that's too large to park on the corner of your desk.

Or perhaps you've hit it lucky. You've picked up a big collection at a garage sale, yet the quality of the pieces vary from junkyard dogs to immaculate recent releases. How do you sort through this mess and what do you do with each vehicle?

Most collectors do not remove the cars and trucks from their original packaging to maintain optimum value to the piece. What you do with your toy vehicles can be more important than how you find and acquire them. Here are some of the basics.

Storage and Display

Several manufacturers make plastic and wooden display cases just for toy cars and trucks. But of course, any carpenter can create a custom case to fit your own needs. Many collectors will just use thumbtacks to hang blister packs to a bulletin board or wall. If you are going to have fun collecting, displaying your collection needs to be a priority.

Rotating your display helps protect against long-term direct sunlight that will fade a car's color.

Caring for your cars and trucks is important in retaining their value to you and for their future value to others. So no matter which route

Many collectors will use thumbtacks to display blister packs on a wall.

you go with a piece—
display or storage—the
less a toy vehicle is han-
dled, the better off it will
be.

Some collectors use
cotton gloves when they
handle unpackaged or
loose vintage and prized
pieces. Always wash
your hands thoroughly
before touching your
collectibles with your
bare hands. Avoid
touching bare die-cast
metal with your fingers,
as the oils, acids and
salts from your skin will
cause them to tarnish
over time. The chemicals

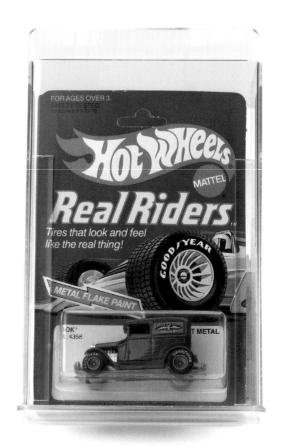

Companies make plastic containers specifically to hold cars in their blister packages.

in your hand can have the same effect on your car as the salt placed
on snowy and icy roads decays real cars. Decals are more easily dam-

Cases of all kinds can be used to display a collection.

aged than the metal of a car, so try to avoid touching them.

Some collectors have found that jewelry boxes make great transportation boxes, with one small car or truck fitting nicely in each compartment.

Collectors should spend a few dollars to protect those cars destined for longtime storage. Plastic clam shells for blister packs and small plastic boxes for even 1:64 scale loose cars are popular storage options. The plastic clam shells for blister packs store nicely in a copier paper box. If nothing else, collectors can use small plastic bags to help keep their cars safe.

Die-cast cars of all kinds should be kept in something, from molded plastic cases just for cars to multi-use plastic bags, to protect them from the elements.

Don't store your car collection in the attic. Cars should be kept in a dry, dust-free environment, where the temperatures don't vary greatly. Dust can easily scratch or damage their finish. Moisture and temperature changes can easily cause the metal in your cars to deteriorate.

Some types of cars may need special handling. For example, some Coke toys have built-in batteries that should be removed. The batteries tend to not only corrode the car's paint, but also the ones around them. And some older cars and trucks need to be separated from their original boxes. The very collectible boxes weren't built to stand the test of time and were printed on high-acidity card stock. The acid in paper will turn decals yellow and eventually even disintegrate rubber treads. One alternative is to use a small plastic bag as a liner, and keep the car in the box.

Restoration

Not every car you add to your collection will be in Mint condition, but there are means to improving the appearance of your collectible car or truck.

Some will need cleaning, but be careful. You don't really want to open a miniature car wash and run your collectible through jet streams of water. Generally, the less water the better. Sometimes you'll pick up a vintage truck that has been played with and your only choice is to give it a quick bath. No matter how much water you use, soft bristle toothbrushes can be used to get into the cracks and crevices. The older the toothbrush, the better. The bristles will get even softer with age and use. Keep your toothbrushes away from decals, however.

Many collectors will use a little bit of glass cleaner on their car, which will give their toy vehicles a new shine. Polishing compounds and even car wax–yes, the same polishing compound used on the car you drive to work each day–is also used by many collectors on their toy vehicles. The wax really does help restore die-cast cars to their original brilliance, though you might want to give a wax job to the least valuable pieces of your collection until you are satisfied with the process. Most collectors use a cotton swab to apply the wax, moving lightly and in a circular motion.

This truck's value will increase if cases of bottles from a donor piece are added.

Some vehicles, especially some of the older Coke trucks, have parts that can break or fall off. You can use a little glue to fix these pieces, but the less glue used the better. If you try to sell or trade a repaired truck, be sure to mention the fix-it job. Many collectors will value the piece less if it has been broken.

Cars often can be repaired using pieces from donor cars, and the combination can drastically increase the condition and value of the remaining car. Tires are the best donor parts, though sometimes pieces such as cases of Coca-Cola bottles will work, too.

Collectors are free to go beyond cleaning and repairing, but it's important to keep your goals in mind when making decisions about major restoration.

If you try to sell or trade a repaired truck, be sure to mention the fix-it job. Many collectors will value the piece less if it has been broken.

For instance, cars can be touched up with a paint job, making small chips and nicks disappear. It can be expensive, but you can even give your die-cast car an entirely new paint job and make it look practically brand new. Of course, unless a collector is experienced at painting die-cast cars, odds are their paint job will do more damage than good.

Most paint jobs, if done by an outside party, would cost more than the value of the vast majority of Coke cars and trucks. Paint jobs are probably best for those collectors who have a truck that they have a great attraction to and plan to keep forever, such as the original truck they used and abused as a child or the car that got them into collecting.

Collectors who are interested in eventually selling their collection should probably stay away from paint jobs. If they do sell or trade their cars, they need to let the potential new owner know of the restoration steps taken.

Insurance

No matter how big or small the size of your collection, you should consider insuring your valuables in case of theft, fire, flood or any other kind of destruction. Cherished collectibles usually can't be replaced in the heart, but that doesn't mean the disaster has to be an entire loss.

Collectors often can get a new lease on life if they have had the proper insurance on their collection. A well-funded collector can get right back in the hunt, often with a much better idea of chasing down all those items on the new want list.

Obtaining insurance on your collection isn't difficult, especially if you house your collectibles at your home. Talk to your agent about the specifics of your collection. In many cases, a small collection will already be covered under your current homeowners insurance. But the bigger and more valuable the collection, the more insurance you'll need.

Many policies insure specific categories of items, such as a toy car and truck collection, only up to a certain amount. If your collection's value is above that amount, you can "schedule" out specific items and insure those separately. Some companies even offer special collector's insurance that requires a professional appraisal. If your collection is big enough, going through this process can be well worth it. Even if you have to get an addendum or rider added to your current policy, it is easily done and affordable.

Renters who keep their collection at home should make sure they have renter's insurance.

Collectors should keep accurate records of their collection, including purchase prices and receipts. In addition, maintain an inventory checklist and photograph your collection. Keep these in a safe place, away from the collection, so that you will have your records if disaster strikes.

Bulletins from the Standardization Committee of Bottlers of Coca-Cola

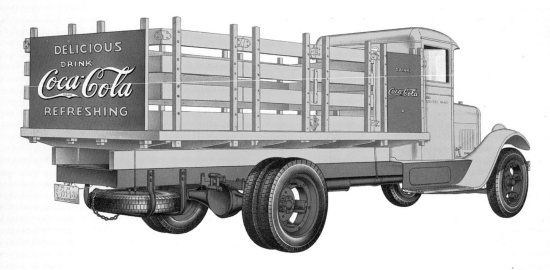

STANDARDIZATION COMMITTEE
OF BOTTLERS OF
Coca-Cola

July, 1938

Bulletin No. 3

Subject:
TRUCK PAINTING

DELICIOUS
DRINK
Coca-Cola
TRADE MARK
REFRESHING

DRINK
Coca-Cola

STANDARD TRUCK PAINTING DESIGN
STAKE BODY
COPY AVAILABLE IN TRANSFERS
SALESMAN'S NAME AND TRUCK NUMBER ON DOOR—OPTIONAL

For SHERWIN-WILLIAMS Painting Instructions See "TRUCK PAINTING" BULLETIN NO. 4
For DuPONT Painting Instructions See "TRUCK PAINTING" BULLETIN NO. 5

1938

Organized in 1924, the Standardization Committee of Bottlers of Coca-Cola was and still is charged with setting uniform standards for equipment for the bottlers of Coca-Cola. The Standardization Committee's decisions regarding truck fleet insignia design and lettering set Coca-Cola apart from other soda products. The colors and insignia chosen by the committee made Coke vehicles easy to identify, whether in Boston, Seattle, Dallas or even Atlanta.

STANDARDIZATION BULLETIN

Bulletin No. 1
Page No. 3
January, 1948

STANDARDIZATION COMMITTEE OF BOTTLERS OF

Subject: **TRUCK PAINTING**

DRINK
Coca-Cola

THE COCA-COLA BOTTLING CO., INC.

STANDARD TRUCK PAINTING DESIGN
STAKE BODY
OTHER COPY AVAILABLE IN TRANSFERS
SALESMAN'S NAME AND TRUCK NUMBER ON DOOR—OPTIONAL

For Painting Instructions See "TRUCK PAINTING" BULLETIN NO. 1, pages 5 and 6

1948

STANDARDIZATION BULLETIN

STANDARDIZATION COMMITTEE OF BOTTLERS OF *Coca-Cola*

Subject: **TRUCK PAINTING**

STANDARD TRUCK PAINTING DESIGN
PANEL BODY
OTHER COPY AVAILABLE IN TRANSFERS
SALESMAN'S NAME AND TRUCK NUMBER ON DOOR—OPTIONAL

For Painting Instructions See "TRUCK PAINTING" BULLETIN NO. 1, pages 5 and 6

1948

STANDARDIZATION BULLETIN

STANDARDIZATION COMMITTEE OF BOTTLERS OF

Subject: TRUCK PAINTING

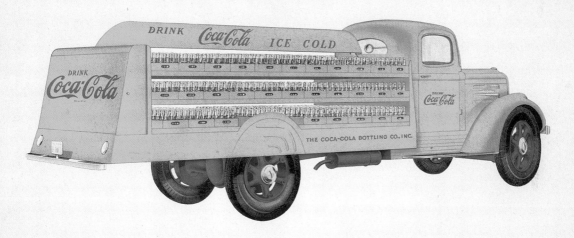

STANDARD TRUCK PAINTING DESIGN

OTHER COPY AVAILABLE IN TRANSFERS
SALESMAN'S NAME AND TRUCK NUMBER ON DOOR—OPTIONAL

For Painting Instructions See "TRUCK PAINTING" BULLETIN NO. 1, pages 5 and 6

1948

STANDARDIZATION BULLETIN

Bulletin No. 1
Page No. 4
January, 1948

STANDARDIZATION COMMITTEE OF BOTTLERS OF

Subject : **TRUCK PAINTING**

STANDARD TRUCK PAINTING DESIGN
SALESMAN'S CAR
OTHER COPY AVAILABLE IN TRANSFERS
SALESMAN'S NAME AND TRUCK NUMBER ON DOOR—OPTIONAL

For Painting Instructions See "TRUCK PAINTING" BULLETIN NO. 1, pages 5 and 6

1949

STANDARDIZATION BULLETIN

Bulletin No. 1
Page No. 4
(Revised)
August, 1949

STANDARDIZATION COMMITTEE OF BOTTLERS OF

Subject: TRUCK PAINTING

STANDARD TRUCK PAINTING DESIGN
SALESMAN'S CAR
OTHER COPY AVAILABLE IN TRANSFERS
SALESMAN'S NAME AND TRUCK NUMBER ON DOOR—OPTIONAL

For Painting Instructions See "TRUCK PAINTING" BULLETIN NO. 1, pages 5 and 6

1949

STANDARDIZATION BULLETIN

Bulletin No. 1
Page No. 3
(*Revised*)
August, 1949

STANDARDIZATION COMMITTEE OF BOTTLERS OF

Subject: **TRUCK PAINTING**

STANDARD TRUCK PAINTING DESIGN
STAKE BODY
OTHER COPY AVAILABLE IN TRANSFERS
SALESMAN'S NAME AND TRUCK NUMBER ON DOOR—OPTIONAL

For Painting Instructions See "TRUCK PAINTING" BULLETIN NO. 1, pages 5 and 6

1949

STANDARDIZATION BULLETIN

Bulletin No. 1
Page No. 2
(Revised)
August, 1949

STANDARDIZATION COMMITTEE OF BOTTLERS OF

Subject: **TRUCK PAINTING**

STANDARD TRUCK PAINTING DESIGN
PANEL BODY
OTHER COPY AVAILABLE IN TRANSFERS

SALESMAN'S NAME AND TRUCK NUMBER ON DOOR—OPTIONAL

For Painting Instructions See "TRUCK PAINTING" BULLETIN NO. 1, pages 5 and 6

1949

STANDARDIZATION BULLETIN

STANDARDIZATION COMMITTEE OF BOTTLERS OF

Subject: STANDARD TRUCK BODY

REAR, SIDE VIEW, DOORS CLOSED

1949